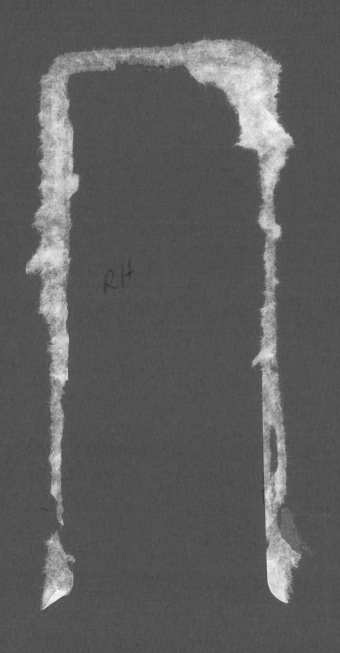

This is a collection of nine folk tales which come from various parts of the Greek world. A mixture of romance and harsh, earthy wisdom makes them particularly satisfying, and yet surprises abound. The humor is wry, the insights are acute, and the flavor is truly Greek.

The author has spent time in Greece, and she collected these stories as she traveled. Marjorie Auerbach, too, has traveled in Greece. Her striking woodcuts beautifully capture the spirit of Greek folklore.

BEWARE THE MAN WITHOUT A BEARD

ALFRED A. KNOPF • NEW YORK

Beware the Man Without a Beard

and Other Greek Folk Tales

retold by ROSE NEUFELD

woodcuts by Marjorie Auerbach

APR 1 6 1969

398.2049
Neu
c.1

THIS IS A BORZOI BOOK
PUBLISHED BY ALFRED A. KNOPF, INC.

Copyright © 1969 by Rose Neufeld
All rights reserved under International and Pan-American Copyright
Conventions. Published in the United States by Alfred A. Knopf, Inc.,
New York, and simultaneously in Canada by Random House of Canada
Limited, Toronto. Distributed by Random House, Inc., New York.

Library of Congress Catalog Card Number: 68–15323

Manufactured in the United States of America

Beware the Man Without a Beard

and Other Greek Folk Tales

retold by ROSE NEUFELD

woodcuts by Marjorie Auerbach

THIS IS A BORZOI BOOK
PUBLISHED BY ALFRED A. KNOPF, INC.

Copyright © 1969 by Rose Neufeld
All rights reserved under International and Pan-American Copyright
Conventions. Published in the United States by Alfred A. Knopf, Inc.,
New York, and simultaneously in Canada by Random House of Canada
Limited, Toronto. Distributed by Random House, Inc., New York.

Library of Congress Catalog Card Number: 68–15323

Manufactured in the United States of America

To my husband Bill,
whose encouragement and love of adventure
helped make this book possible

Contents

BEWARE THE MAN WITHOUT A BEARD

Golden Wand

It was on the eve of the new year in the town of Patras, long ago, that a rich merchant sat at supper with his three daughters. Now, although the three maidens were handsome, there was a great difference among them. The two older sisters, Katina and Despina, were spiteful and cruel while the youngest, Tula, was sweet and friendly. Besides, she far surpassed her two older sisters in beauty and grace.

After they finished their meal, all waited expectantly for the cook to bring in the *vassilopita*, the New Year's cake, with its lucky gold coin. When the cake finally arrived, the merchant cut a slice for each daughter, but it was Katina, the oldest, who joyfully cried, "I have it! I found the gold coin in my piece of cake!"

Tula was deeply disappointed because she had hoped to get the lucky coin, which would bring her good fortune and help ease her loneliness. For, in their envy, her two sisters shunned and ignored her. Nevertheless, she congratulated Katina, as did everyone else.

Later that night, Tula and her sisters stole down to the kitchen, where the cook gave them some yeast she had saved from the *vassilopita*.

"Remember, girls," said the cook, "salt the yeast heavily so that your sleep will be disturbed by thirst. The man who gives you water in your dreams is the man destined to be your husband."

Hurrying to their rooms, the girls eagerly swallowed the salted yeast. They fell asleep, each one hoping to catch a glimpse of her future husband.

The next morning, the three sisters sat talking in the garden.

"Well," said Katina, "my gold coin has already begun to bring me luck. The man who gave me water in my dreams was Costas, the richest farmer in Patras. I shall probably be married within the year."

Despina could hardly wait to tell her dream. Giggling and gushing, she said, "The man who gave me water was Adonis, the handsomest man in our town. I, too, shall probably be married within the year."

"Now you, Tula," said Katina and Despina together. "Tell us

your dream. Tell us who gave you water."

Tula hung her head and said nothing. Her sisters prodded her until she said in a low voice, "I dreamt about a golden wand."

"A golden wand!" roared Katina and Despina. "Oh, you poor fool!" They shrieked with laughter at their little sister, who fled to her room to escape their tormenting.

When the great feast of Epiphany came a few days later, the sisters watched their father's ship being blessed. The merchant was preparing to journey to the Indies and, as was his custom, he asked his daughters what kind of gifts they wanted. Katina begged him to bring her a dress of the finest silk. Despina pleaded for a turban woven of silver thread. Tula beseeched him, "Oh, Father, please search for a golden wand and bring it to me!"

"I shall try, my child," sighed her father, caressing the unhappy girl.

Many months went by and Tula wondered what news her father would bring upon his return. Her sisters still scoffed and jeered at her because of her strange dream. But Tula held her tongue and said nothing.

At last, on a fine day in spring, the merchant's ship sailed into the harbor at Patras. His daughters flew about the house arranging everything for their father's comfort.

Soon the weary merchant was in his own home surrounded by his family. He distributed the gifts, to the delight of Katina and Despina. Tula bit her lips with impatience as she watched the others open their presents and heard her father tell of his many adventures. Finally, he turned to her and said, "Yes, my child, I have something for you, too. This cup, ring, and letter from Golden Wand. That is the name of a handsome prince, both kind and clever. After much searching, I found him in a huge palace. When he heard of your dream, he showed me the picture of the girl he had seen in his dreams. It was a portrait of you, Tula. Now my daughter, go to your room, for you must read your letter alone."

Radiant with joy, Tula sped to her chamber, locked the door, and tore open her letter. Katina, however, overcome with jealousy and curiosity, followed her and peeked through the keyhole. Unaware Katina was watching, Tula read:

"My Darling, if you wish to see me, put water in the cup your father will give you, then put the ring in the cup. Say three times, 'Come, my Golden Wand.' A dove will fly in from an opening you must leave in your window. The dove will wash in the water and become a man."

Still unaware that Katina was watching, Tula quickly removed a small glass pane from her window. Then she followed the instructions in her letter. Just as promised a white dove flew in, bathed in the cup, and was transformed into a magnificent prince.

The charming young prince bowed and introduced himself as Golden Wand. He and Tula spoke for many hours with the affection and devotion of a couple long known to one another. When it was time for Golden Wand to leave, he touched the water in the cup and became a dove again. Just before flying away, the dove dropped a red berry at Tula's feet, telling her to cut it open and put on what she found inside. With a tiny, sharp knife Tula cut open the berry and took out a gown so dazzling as to rival any she had ever seen. She put on this dress

of gold, embroidered with rubies, emeralds, and sapphires, and paraded with delight in front of her mirror.

By now Katina was burning with fierce envy. She, too, wanted the handsome Golden Wand to present her with such a splendid dress. Tomorrow, she thought, I will summon the prince and see what kind of gift he will have for me.

True to her vow, the next morning Katina left her sisters sewing in the garden, saying she was going to search for her scissors. She hastily ran to Tula's room, where she took the cup and ring and proceeded to do everything her sister had done. But in her greed, Katina failed to notice the tiny, sharp knife Tula had left in the cup. When the dove came and bathed in the water, he gashed himself. Terrified, he flew away, bleeding profusely.

The panic-stricken Katina replaced the cup filled with blood in the cupboard. Flustered and frightened, she rejoined her sisters, explaining her discomfiture as vexation over the lost scissors.

Later, Tula returned to her room, somewhat uneasy about Katina's peculiar behavior. Her fears were justified when she opened her cupboard and saw the cup with blood in it. Trembling with fear and dread, she tried to summon Golden Wand, but the dove did not come. She wept bitterly, realizing what Katina must have done when she disappeared from the garden that morning.

Tula would not be consoled till her father arranged for her to sail to the Indies to see Golden Wand. When she arrived after a long voyage, she followed the same road her father had taken many months before.

As she hurried along, she saw a dove circling above her.

Surely, she thought, Golden Wand has sent this bird to help me. Then the dove spoke to her.

"The prince is dying, but he can be saved if you cover his wounds with an ointment made from the bark of the cornel tree and water from the spring just outside the castle."

Tula did as the dove had advised her and, disguising herself as a physician, she presented herself to the king. The frantic monarch agreed to let this solemn young physician try to heal his son, since none of the court doctors were having any success.

For seven days Tula applied the magic ointment to the gashes in Golden Wand's throat. By the eighth day, the prince was completely cured, much to the joy of his father and all the court.

"Physician," said the grateful king, "you shall have whatever you desire. Name your wish."

"Sire," answered Tula, "I ask only that you hold a banquet tonight for all your court in honor of Golden Wand."

"What you ask is small indeed; it shall be done," said the king.

That night a thousand candles twinkled and gleamed in the palace as the guests assembled for the banquet. When everyone had finished the feast, Tula, still disguised, asked the king for permission to tell a tale.

The king granted her request, and a silence fell in the great hall as she rose and told the remarkable story of the love of Tula for Golden Wand. She explained how Katina had wounded Golden Wand and how Tula had undertaken the journey to save the prince. Finally, she told of the physician and the success of the magic ointment. With the last of her words, Tula flung aside her mantle and, instead of the physician, there stood the maiden clad in the wondrous golden gown the prince had given her.

Golden Wand was overcome with joy as Tula fell into his arms.

"Ah, my dearest love," he said. "I thought I should never see your fair face again!"

The two young lovers begged the king for permission to marry the next day. The delighted monarch granted the request and ordered a splendid wedding celebration for all the people in the realm.

A wedding feast, the like of which had never before been seen, was held amidst rejoicings and blessings. The prince took Tula to a beautiful castle where they lived long in love and happiness, and where her father and sisters visited the royal pair on many occasions.

Beware the
Man Without a Beard

Long ago, on the island of Pontos, a poor peasant lay dying. Since he had no money to leave his young son, Spiros, he wanted to bestow some wisdom on the boy to help him make his way in the world.

"My son," gasped the dying father, "heed my words. If you wish to avoid disaster in your dealings, beware the man without a beard. If you meet such a man on the road return home, as your journey will not be successful. If a beardless man greets you, do not return his greeting."

The lad promised his father he would follow his advice. And so the poor old peasant died peacefully.

After some months had passed, Spiros set out on his first journey to the market place, a long distance away. With him was his horse, laden with olives. Just after he had passed the halfway mark on the road, he saw a beardless man approaching from the opposite direction.

"Good day to you, my fine young lad," called out the beardless man.

Spiros remembered his father's advice.

"Your good day and you may go and be buried together," he shouted rudely. He then turned around and hurried home.

The next day Spiros and the horse, laden with olives, set out again for the market.

Once more he found himself facing the beardless man on the road.

"Good day to you, my fine young lad," sang out the beardless man.

"Good day," muttered Spiros cautiously.

"These olives, are they not for sale?" asked the beardless man.

"Yes, they are, but I won't trade with a beardless man. My father warned me against this with his dying breath."

"Ho, ho, my fine lad," laughed the man, "don't you know that you are in a place full of beardless men? From here to the market place there are no others to be found. Now sell me the olives and I will give you a good price."

Spiros considered for a moment. Since he had never been very far from home, he was not sure about the truth of what the

beardless man had told him. After some thought, he agreed to the sale.

The two made a bargain and decided on the price of eighty *drachmas*. They then went to the barn of the beardless man, where Spiros unloaded the olives. As he started to lead his horse away, the man roughly pushed him aside.

"Just a minute," he snarled, "I bought the olives and the horse as well for the eighty *drachmas*."

With these words, the beardless man led the horse into the barn and locked the door. Tears came to Spiros' eyes. But the boy realized he could do nothing, for the man was so much bigger and stronger than he. Spiros took his money and went home with a heavy heart.

When he arrived home, the boy told his mother how he had been cheated and robbed of their horse. She wept bitterly at first, then chided her son for disobeying his father's counsel. A few days later she called to him saying, "Spiros, you must load our little donkey with these baskets of olives and make the journey to the market. I will give you our last two gold coins. With the money from the olives and the gold you must buy another horse."

Once again Spiros set out for the market place, this time accompanied by his little donkey. Hardly had he passed the half-way mark when he saw the beardless man coming toward him.

"Well, well, my fine young lad, off to the market again, eh?" sneered the beardless man, grasping Spiros' arm so hard that the boy cried out in pain.

Then the beardless man shouted at Spiros, "I see no need for you to go to the market when you can sell olives to me."

The beardless man glared at the frightened Spiros, seized him, and shook him so hard the lad could hardly breathe.

"Now let's see, how much are these olives worth?" he said.

In spite of his fright, Spiros thought of a plan to save himself from being robbed again. While the beardless man turned to walk around the animal, the boy pushed the gold coins into the donkey's mouth.

As the beardless man looked over the pathetic little creature, Spiros tickled the donkey's nose with a straw. Suddenly the donkey sneezed, and out popped the gold coins. The beardless man gazed with astonishment.

"What is the price of this animal?" he demanded.

"I'm afraid he's very costly, sir. As you see, he sneezes gold."

"Never mind, just tell me the price," the beardless man insisted.

Spiros thought carefully for several minutes while the beardless man studied the donkey in amazement. Finally the boy spoke. "I can let you have him for six hundred *drachmas.*"

Eagerly the beardless man counted out the money and pushed it into Spiros' hand. As the man pulled the donkey away, Spiros called out, "If you want the donkey to sneeze gold all the time, you must put him in the cellar and keep the door nailed closed for forty days and nights. Inside the house, dig a hole down to the cellar and pour water and throw chaff down to him. Afterward, open the cellar, and you will find it full of gold coins."

Dancing with joy, Spiros went home and told his mother of his second meeting with the beardless man. Before she could scold him, the boy showed her the money he had received for the donkey, and promised to go to the market the very next day

15

to buy a fine horse. His mother was delighted with what she thought was her son's wonderful ability as a trader.

To the beardless man and his wife the forthcoming forty days loomed like an eternity. They followed Spiros' instructions except for the feeding of the little donkey. The greedy couple knew the donkey would fatten up more quickly on barley, so they fed him on this grain only. The barley and water soon caused the poor little beast to swell and burst. On the evening of the fortieth day, the beardless man and his wife, trembling with anticipation, opened the cellar door.

Imagine their horror when they found no gold but only a poor dead donkey. Furious, the beardless man ran down the road and across the fields to Spiros' house.

The boy was standing in the garden when he saw the man hurrying toward his home. Spiros guessed that the beardless man had discovered the trick he had played on him. How, he wondered, could he escape the wrath of the beardless man?

"Mother!" he exclaimed, rushing into the kitchen, "When the beardless man comes here and asks for me, you must say I am out in the olive groves. You must tell him you will send our dog to tell me to come home."

With these words, Spiros ran out and found a hiding place in a corner of the yard.

"Where is Spiros?" roared the man, as he flung open the door.

"My dear man," answered the mother calmly, "Spiros is out tending the olive trees, but I will send his dog for him. The dog will tell him to come home so that you may speak with him."

"What!" shouted the beardless man in disbelief. "How can a dog tell him to return?"

"You see," answered the mother, "since we do not have a servant, we simply use our dog. We always send him to the fields with food or messages."

The mother then opened the door and tapped the dog on his tail saying, "Go tell Spiros to come home. This man wants to speak to him."

When Spiros saw his pet running out, he motioned to him. The boy and his dog hid in the yard for a few minutes. Then they went back into the house together.

As soon as the beardless man saw Spiros, he immediately forgot to scold him for tricking him, and quietly said, "I will forgive you, my lad, if you agree to sell me this dog."

"No, never!" protested Spiros. "He is our servant. We wouldn't think of parting with him."

But the man insisted and finally, after arguing with Spiros and his mother for several hours, they made a bargain. The man paid one thousand *drachmas* for the dog.

Singing and whistling, the beardless man arrived home with his latest purchase. Instead of smiles from his wife, however, he got a scolding for allowing himself to be swindled again.

But the beardless man convinced her that this valuable dog would now be their servant. Early next morning, before he left for work, he instructed his wife to put his lunch in a bag around the dog's neck. Then he told her to order the dog to the fields where he would be working.

At the lunch hour, the man's wife opened the door to the house and gave the dog a pat on the tail saying, "Now take the bag of food around your neck and go directly to the corn fields. Your master is waiting for his lunch."

The dog, however, ran out into the yard and down the steps into the cellar. He ate all the food in the bag and calmly went to sleep for the rest of the day.

Meanwhile, the beardless man waited in vain for his meal. When he finally came home in the evening, he shouted angrily at his wife, "Why didn't you send the dog with my food?"

After his wife explained that she had done everything that was told her, the man flew into a rage. He ranted and raved till his face turned purple.

"Tomorrow," his wife told him, "you must go to Spiros and get our money back."

So early the next morning the man set out to see the young Spiros. The lad was out working in the olive groves when he saw the beardless man walking toward his house with Spiros' dog.

Spiros ran home and excitedly told his mother, who was cutting up a freshly killed goat, that the beardless man was on his way there.

"This time we must play a master trick on him," Spiros said to his mother.

While his mother listened, Spiros explained his new idea. He told his mother to take the bladder of the goat and fill it with the goat's blood. Then she was to hang this around her neck. When the beardless man accused him of swindling, Spiros would begin to blame his mother for the trick. The boy asked his mother to pretend to argue with him and Spiros, in a fit of anger, would stab the goat's bladder. Then his mother would sink to the ground as if she were dead.

"Now," Spiros continued, "when you hear me play my pipe,

19

you must rise up and make believe you have come back to life."

They no sooner had everything prepared than the door flew open and in stomped the beardless man roaring, "Swindler! Give me back my thousand *drachmas*. That dog can do nothing!"

At that point the boy and his mother started to accuse each other of the trick. As they argued, Spiros stabbed the bladder, and his mother sank to the ground.

Gasping with horror, the man cried out, "Lad, what have you done? You have killed your mother!"

"Fear not, sir. What I have done in anger can be made right," answered the boy. He then began to play on his pipe smilingly.

His mother stirred, opened her eyes, and rose to her feet.

The astounded man was struck speechless by this miracle. Then he gasped, "Spiros, you swindled me in the past, but I'll forget all that if you will just sell me this pipe."

At first Spiros would not sell, but after a great deal of bargaining, he agreed to part with his pipe for two thousand *drachmas*.

Once again the man went home in a very merry mood. He burst into the house, where he found his wife and her relatives drinking coffee. He proudly showed off his latest purchase.

Much to his surprise, his wife began to weep bitterly.

"Alas," she moaned, "we shall die of hunger. You have been swindled again of all our money."

The beardless man, sure of the magic pipe, decided to teach his wife and her doubting relatives a lesson.

"Stop arguing with me," he yelled and, as he said this, he ran out into the yard. There he snatched up his wife's favorite piglet which she was carefully fattening for a feast. As his horrified wife protested, he stabbed the little animal.

"Dear wife and relatives," he said, pushing them aside. "Please do not be so frightened. Just see what will happen now."

He began to play a gay tune on his pipe. Nothing happened to the dead piglet. And again he played the tune. Still nothing happened. The animal did not stir. The beardless man stopped playing and looked stunned.

"But . . . but the pipe," he stammered. "The piglet is supposed to come back to life."

His wife and her relatives began to beat him severely for his wanton foolishness. After some time, he was able to escape their blows. As he rubbed his wounds, safe at last in the barn, the beardless man thought, "Alas, I have paid too high a price for the horse I took from Spiros."

A Tale of Naxos

The ragged, steep hills of the island of Naxos, rising out of the calm Aegean sea, were once the home of a proud and valorous king. From his magnificent palace he would sally forth at the head of his army of mighty warriors, vanquishing and slaying myriads of his enemies. Though he would return with rich spoils, he never kept anything for himself.

All he needed for his own contentment was the glory and the memory of his exploits. To his army, both officers and soldiers, he distributed the booty from these conquests.

22

But to his dismay, he found that no matter how just he thought he had been, his men regarded his gifts with suspicion and discontent. His people would steal from one another till each one felt he at last owned his neighbor's more valuable share. The monarch constantly sought to calm his subjects' suspicions and discourage their thievery by bestowing the spoils more fairly.

The most daring thief and rogue of all was Andreas. The king hesitated to punish him for his mischief because he was a brave and loyal soldier.

But alas, times changed for the king and his once busy, prosperous subjects. Season after season, drought took its toll of the farms. The grain dried in scorched fields; the olives, grapes, and melons withered and died, leaving little food for the people and their beasts. Day after day the fishermen would cast their nets, but the nets when pulled in were always empty. Their poor wives and children waited every evening in the hope they would bring something home, and despaired when it was only a small, bony fish. The very fish in the sea seemed to have fled from the waters surrounding the island.

The once-proud warriors were reduced to melancholy and silence as they watched their families grow lean and weak from hunger. There was no more thievery or mischief, since there was nothing left to take, and people were much too busy trying to find food.

Powerless to aid his people, the king sank deeper and deeper into despair, until one day he received a request for an audience from the youngest of his commanders, General Kolokonis.

"Your Highness," said the general, "I have heard of a vegetable called a squash, grown near Attica. I am sure we can end our famine if we could only get some of these and seeds to grow more."

A flicker of interest shone in the hollow eyes of the king as he nodded wearily. The eager voice of his young general went on, "We can eat the squash and plant the seeds for a new crop."

For the first time the king raised his head and looked directly at Kolokonis.

"I will order a ship to set sail tonight for Attica! You must persuade the king there to send us this food," the monarch commanded excitedly.

After three weeks had passed, the king himself waited to greet the general as his ship sailed into the harbor. Rushing to greet his sovereign, Kolokonis triumphantly called out, "Your Majesty, all is well! The king of Attica has sent us enough sacks of squash to feed all our people."

For the first time in months the king actually smiled. Then he issued an order calling for all his subjects to assemble in front of his castle.

All day the populace from every corner of Naxos gradually gathered in the courtyard facing the palace. A deep silence fell over the expectant crowd as the king appeared.

"My people," he announced, "the king of Attica has sent us a vegetable and seeds so that we may have food and a new crop. Here it is," said the monarch, holding aloft a gleaming, golden squash. "You can cook it, and plant these seeds in the sacks for a new crop. There are enough sacks here for every family. Just step forward and take them."

To his indignation and amazement, instead of rushing for the

food, the people backed away. Some on the outskirts of the crowd even ran away to the safety of their homes. The king cajoled, pleaded, then commanded his subjects to take the new vegetable, but they refused. The crowd gradually melted away until no one was left in the vast yard but the lone figure of General Kolokonis.

"Well," sighed the dejected king, "what shall we do now?"

But the young general was not discouraged. He promised the king he would devise another plan to distribute the strange, new food to the reluctant, suspicious people.

He took his leave and trudged up the steep, winding paths leading to the summit of the island. On his way, he met a sad, thin Andreas. Kolokonis looked over the roofs of the white-washed cottages to the blue sea far below.

At last he thought of a scheme that caused him to laugh out loud. Jubilantly he hurried back to the palace.

After the king had listened to the general he, too, threw back his head and laughed heartily. Still chuckling, he gave orders to have all the sacks of the seeds and the squashes placed in the center of the main village square. Only the strongest, fiercest soldiers were allowed to guard the sacks.

In the morning, when the people awoke and went about their business, they were surprised by the heavy protection given to these sacks. All day and into the night, only the most ferocious guards maintained their vigil.

All this proved too much of a temptation for the thieving people of Naxos, and Andreas felt especially challenged.

"My friends," he said, "surely the palace guards would not be on duty if these squashes and seeds were not a great deal more valuable than we have been led to believe. We must steal some and see for ourselves."

Led by Andreas, the villagers hid in the dark, scarcely breathing, waiting for the guards to turn away. Then, soundlessly, they cut the sacks open and made off with the golden vegetables and the seeds.

By the third night, the savage-looking soldiers had nothing to guard but slit, empty sacks. The people hurried to cook and eat the precious squashes. They had enough food and, as the king had suggested, they planted the seeds, too. Soon they were able to reap a fine harvest.

Of course, Andreas and all the people did not know that the king had warned his guards only to look fierce but not to act so. They were instructed to turn away often to allow the people to steal the new food.

From being the most miserable of men, the king became one of the merriest. His people prospered again, and he led his army into new, more glorious exploits. As for the young general, he lived to gain much honor and some riches, serving his king and people with wisdom and understanding.

Love Like Salt

Once upon a time there lived in Thrace a proud old king, who had three beautiful daughters. Although this monarch was the possessor of much wealth, he insisted his children be modestly clothed so that their great beauty would not be rivaled by fine jewels and elaborate gowns. The king loved his daughters dearly, and they in turn loved him. However, he had one fault: he was exceedingly vain. One day, to satisfy his vanity, he decided to hear his daughters tell of their devotion to him. He ordered them brought before him.

Izmini, the oldest, was the first to speak.

"Father," she said, "my love for you is like the luscious sweetness of the finest sugar."

The king nodded, satisfied. Next, the second daughter, Sofia, spoke.

"Father, my love for you is like the delicious sweetness of rich, golden honey."

Again the satisfied king nodded. Then came the youngest daughter, Helene. She spoke eagerly.

"Oh, Father, my love for you is like the purest salt."

"What!" roared the shocked, infuriated king. "You ungrateful girl! My other daughters hold me in sweet regard. But you— you shall be punished for daring to insult me with your answer!"

As he strode back and forth in anger, the king by chance glanced out of the palace window. There he saw a young peasant staggering by under a load of firewood. The ragged fellow was so poor he did not own a donkey to carry such burdens.

"For your punishment," raged the king, "I shall marry you to that wretch out there."

The guards were ordered to fetch the wood seller to the throne room. The monarch ordered the marriage to take place immediately. When the ceremony was over, he warned Helene and the frightened peasant, called Panos, never to return.

Panos took the weeping princess home to his miserable hut. There they lived as best they could. As the days went by, Helene realized that though Panos was pitifully poor, he was a kind and gentle man. She learned to love him and, in spite of the fact that they lived in poverty, their marriage was harmonious and happy.

About a year later, Panos met some merchants who were going on a distant journey. They promised him wealth if he would join them, and this he decided to do. Just before leaving, Helene asked him to fetch some water from the well.

As Panos drew the bucket up he saw a horrible shape clinging to its side. It was Tchemontis, the demon of the well, an ugly, bad-tempered creature. Tchemontis said nothing, but glared at Panos belligerently.

"Good day to you, friend, and how are you?" said Panos kindly, feeling sorry for any creature so ugly.

The demon at first said nothing, then it croaked, "Because you have spoken kindly, I shall give you three magic pomegranates. Guard them carefully and never open them unless you are alone."

With these words Tchemontis vanished, leaving Panos frightened and shaken but in possession of three large, ripe pomegranates. He hurried home and told Helene of his strange experience. Before departing, he gave her one of the fruits and repeated the demon's warning. With the other two pomegranates in his knapsack, Panos went off to seek his fortune with the merchants.

Shortly after her husband left, Helene gave birth to a son whom she called Nikos. She and her baby lived in bitter poverty until an accident changed their fate. Helene by chance dropped the demon's pomegranate on the stone floor, and the fruit was dashed open. Her eyes bulged with amazement as she stared at the sight at her feet. From out of the split shells poured large, sparkling jewels.

With this treasure Helene built a beautiful palace and a

fountain surrounded by cool, green gardens so that those pass-
ing by could rest and quench their thirst.

Many years went by, and one day Panos returned to the
village. But when he searched for his miserable hut he found
instead a palace. At the window, he saw his wife sitting beside a
handsome youth. Panos' heart filled with bitterness at the
thought of his wife remarrying. Helene, however, soon noticed
him and flew to embrace him. To the youth beside her she said,
"Come and kiss your father's hand, Nikos. He has come home
to us at last."

Panos then understood that this handsome young man was
the son he had never seen. They all embraced with tears of joy.

"But . . . but how did you manage to build this palace?"
asked the bewildered Panos.

Helene reminded Panos of the magic pomegranate he had left
with her. Panos had forgotten the fruit, and indeed he still had
the other two in his old, worn knapsack. When he was alone
later that night, he dashed the second pomegranate open on the
stone floor.

Once again the miracle occurred. From out of the shattered
fruit there poured huge gleaming jewels.

With these gems Panos and Helene built a dazzling palace
even larger than the first. White marble, gold, and silver
glistened in the sunlight. All who beheld this rare sight were
struck with wonder and awe. The gardens around the palace
were filled with fragrant flowers of every color in the rainbow.
Tall green trees gave shade and coolness to all who sat beneath
them.

Those who passed on the road in front of the palace were in-

vited to refresh themselves at the large fountain, bubbling with clear, cold water.

The poor were not forgotten, either. For them, Panos and Helene provided a shop, where they gave to all who asked delicious sweetmeats and fruits. Many a poor peasant had his fill of *halva, loukoum,* and *baklava.* The orchards yielded tempting grapes, watermelons, apples, oranges, and lemons. While Panos and Helene knew contentment, they sought to give aid constantly to others less fortunate. As for Nikos, he was the happy possessor of the third magic pomegranate, to be opened only after his marriage.

In time, the news of the charitable deeds of Panos and Helene reached Helene's father, the proud and vain old king. He decided to see for himself the couple who were doing so much good for others. He and his courtiers journeyed to the magnificent palace, where they were welcomed by Panos and Helene. The king did not recognize his own daughter and son-in-law because of the many years that had gone by since their banishment. Also, Panos and Helene were dressed in fine clothes and blazing jewels, which changed their appearance and made them look very grand.

Helene invited her father and his court to a banquet in their great hall. Before they dined, Panos entertained the guests, while Helene busied herself in the kitchen giving important and strange orders to the cook. The cook, though bewildered, listened carefully to Helene's unusual directions, and promised to prepare the food according to these new ways.

At last the food was ready. Into the huge banquet room came

servants carrying immense silver platters of brown, crackling roasted lamb, gleaming white rice piled high, rich red tomatoes, and many other tempting dishes. The king and guests could hardly wait to begin the feast, but after a few bites everyone stopped eating.

Helene, who sat next to the king, turned to him and inquired, "Is something wrong, Your Majesty?"

"Yes, indeed," he replied, "this food is not fit to eat! It is not salted!"

Helene then signalled the servants, who cleared the tables. Once again they brought more food. They carried in platters of the delicious roasted meat and heaping bowls of vegetables. This time the old king and all the guests ate with great gusto.

At the end of the meal the king turned to Helene and said, "My dear, we could not eat the first course at all, but the food we have just finished was delicious because it was properly salted. Food without salt, you know, is worthless."

"Oh, my father!" cried Helene. "You drove me away when I told you that my love for you was like salt. Yet now, after these many years, you have finally understood what I meant."

The old king was astonished to hear these words. His joy at learning that the master and mistress of this palace were his own daughter and son-in-law was boundless. He wept with joy for a long time, and his courtiers wept, too.

"Yes," he said at last, "salt is more desirable than sugar and more important than honey."

34

From then on, the old king never again doubted the value of salt, nor his daughter's love. They all decided to forget the time of the cruel banishment, and agreed instead to live happily together in love and contentment.

The Greater Sinner

Many years ago in the time of our grandfathers' grandfathers, there lived on the island of Lemnos a cruel and merciless bandit called Yanis. Just the mention of his name was enough to strike terror in the hearts of the farmers and shepherds who listened to tales of his savage deeds. At the sight of his fierce, black mustache twitching with impatience, his victims would faint, never offering the slightest resistance.

One day, Yanis sat alone on the steep cliffs overlooking the sea. A great sadness came over him as he realized how much suffering his life of evil had caused others. He felt a deep long-ing to repent and redeem himself in the eyes of God and man.

That very day he decided to abandon his hideaway, with its weapons and horde of gold. Taking nothing but the clothing he wore, he journeyed to the village of Koudopoulin, where he sought the advice of a very wise old priest. Yanis begged for help in gaining pardon from God for his life of sin and crime.

After Yanis had spoken, the priest sat in silence, so moved was he by the earnest pleas of the bandit. After much thought he spoke.

"First," he said, "you must give up your life of sin and banditry forever. Next, you must promise that from this day on you will pray every morning and evening of every day and ask God for pardon. Lastly, you must plant a garden with fruit and vegetables that will provide you with your food. In this garden you must also plant a withered twig from an olive tree. Water this twig faithfully; care for it devotedly. When God has seen fit to pardon you, then will this twig sprout leaves."

And so, on the outskirts of the village in a field near a spring, Yanis built himself a simple hut. He prayed every morning and evening of every day. On the day of the Feast of the Forty Saints he dug a garden three spades deep. He sowed his seeds of fruits and vegetables, taking care also to plant a withered olive twig on one corner of his plot.

Many months went by and the garden flourished. Melons, pumpkins, apples, and figs grew in abundance. To those who passed by and perchance stopped to rest, Yanis gave cool, clear water from the spring and fruits from his garden. He always refused payment, saying he was doing good deeds to redeem his soul. Never did he forget his prayers, nor did he ever falter in his care of the twig. But though he watered it faithfully, much to his disappointment not so much as a tiny bud appeared.

One very hot afternoon, Yanis looked up from his work and saw a man running toward him. In one hand the stranger carried a great fearsome ax. Even from a distance Yanis could see how dusty and ragged the man looked. Thinking how hot and tired the stranger must be, Yanis quickly filled a cup with water and seized a juicy melon, preparing to offer the stranger food and drink.

As the man approached and saw Yanis in his path, he screamed, "Out of my way, you fool!"

Yanis hesitated for a moment, hardly believing his ears. Seeing Yanis' hesitation only seemed to enrage the stranger further. He lifted the ax and, with eyes rolling wildly, he struck at Yanis. The amazed Yanis dropped the refreshments and leaped nimbly aside.

"Wait, wait!" he cried. "I mean you no harm."

But the stranger would not listen; he seemed beyond reason, and once again he lifted the ax to swing at Yanis. Ducking once more, Yanis managed to avoid the ax. Thinking quickly how to save his life, Yanis struck the stranger a powerful blow that felled him. When Yanis bent to look at the man, he saw at once that he had killed him.

"Oh, what have I done!" he wailed, beating his breast. "Now I will never be pardoned for my sins! I can never be consoled!"

With a heavy heart, he went to the village to find the priest and tell him what had happened.

After listening to the story the priest said, "We must find out

who this stranger was, and why he acted so peculiarly. Come, let us ask the people of Koudopoulin if they know anything of this."

Together they went to the village square where, to the surprise of Yanis, there were several elders who seemed to know something of this stranger.

"We must go to the field where we can see this man for ourselves," they said.

They all went to the field where the stranger lay dead.

"Yes, it is the same man," they murmured to one another. "Oh, yes, we know of him."

"Tell us then," said the priest. "Who was the stranger, and why was he here?"

Each one of the elders then told something of this unusual tale.

"This man was one who was skilled at building and repairing water pipes. In spite of his great abilities, he was greedy and selfish beyond imagination. Yesterday he tried to destroy our village's water supply with his ax, but he was discovered. Undoubtedly he would have tried again tonight. Tomorrow, when we would be desperate for water for ourselves and our beasts, he would offer to repair the pipe immediately, at a tremendous price. Of course, then we would be at his mercy and would have no choice but to pay him."

When the elders finished the explanation, all stood in silence for a few moments, looking at the dead man. Yanis by chance glanced at his dried twig, planted so many months ago.

"Father! Look!" he shouted excitedly. "Look at the olive twig."

All eyes turned and beheld not the dried, scorched twig, but a slender, green branch with glossy leaves that glowed with a promise of vitality and fruitfulness.

Before the hushed and bewildered group, Yanis fell to his knees.

The priest stood before him and said, "Here lies the greater sinner, this evil man, who wanted to cut off our water supply. In accidentally stopping him from carrying out his wicked plan you did not sin, but instead saved our village. And now, God has seen fit to pardon you."

Tears fell from Yanis' eyes as he thanked God for forgiveness and for sending this sign of his pardon. The villagers also did not forget Yanis. Gradually they overcame their fear and suspicion of him, making him welcome in their homes. He became a godfather to many of the village children and his life was filled with happiness. But Yanis never forgot his prayers, nor did he forget to tend the olive branch, symbol of his pardon and redemption.

The Silent Princess

Many years ago, there lived in Thessaloniki a prince who was joyous, brave, and determined of heart. One day this handsome young prince was strolling about enjoying the fine air, when by chance he met an old friend. His friend, a much traveled merchant, had just returned from a journey to Alexandroupolis. In the course of their conversation, the merchant showed the prince a picture of a beautiful girl. The heart of the prince sang with joy as he gazed at the portrait of the lovely young maiden.

"Ah, Prince Philippos, I see you are much taken with the picture of the Princess Izmini. She is indeed one of the fairest in the land. Such grace, such delicacy! This picture hardly does her justice. You may win her hand in marriage, too, but for one vexing problem."

"And what might be the cause of this vexation?" asked the prince.

"A year ago, Izmini's father ordered her to choose a husband from among three rich old monarchs who had asked for her hand. The princess refused, vowing she would remain silent and unwed till her father could find a suitor who would be able to make her break her vow of silence. Needless to say, the three original suitors could not. Since then, many from far and near have tried, but Izmini is as wily as she is beautiful. No one has yet succeeded."

Prince Philippos smiled, to the merchant's surprise.

"I can see the princess is worthy of all my efforts. For you see, this will make the prize even more valuable when I have won!"

Saying this, Philippos hurried to his own castle, where he bade his parents farewell. He mounted his black stallion and rode away toward Alexandroupolis, thinking of how to win the silent princess.

As the prince went through the town, he passed the market place where he noticed a crowd buying birds. When a tiny gray sparrow was offered for sale, there were no purchasers. Moved by pity for the shabby little bird, the prince bought it for one *drachma*.

As he galloped away on the open road, he looked down at the bird bobbing in its cage on his saddle.

"I think I have made a foolish purchase of the little bird," he said softly.

"Master, please don't think you have been swindled," said a small voice.

"Who speaks?" shouted the astonished Philippos, wheeling to a sudden halt.

"It is only I, Master, your sparrow, here beside you. I can speak with the voice of a man. Now that I am yours, you will be lucky and gain whatever you desire."

The amazed prince continued his journey while becoming better acquainted with his magic little bird. Soon he explained how he had fallen in love with the picture of Princess Izmini and was on his way to win her hand if he could make her speak.

"This is what you must do, Master," said the sparrow. "Conceal me in your hand when you enter Izmini's room. Pretend to examine the wooden chest there and put me into it. Speak to the princess, but don't show surprise when she remains silent. Then say 'good evening' three times to the chest. Ask the chest to tell you a story to amuse you. I will answer, and at the end of my story the princess will speak."

Philippos agreed to this plan and impatiently spurred his horse onward. When the prince arrived at the palace, he saw a long line of disappointed suitors straggling away. Undaunted, he alighted and walked into the king's throne room. He greeted the king and made known his desire to win the hand of Princess Izmini. The king wearily consented without even a second glance at the confident young man.

That evening Philippos went to Izmini's chamber, where he found three old hags dressed in black seated outside the door.

"The king sent us here," they cackled at him, "so that we may hear the princess if she speaks to you."

Philippos bowed gallantly to them, then knocked lightly and opened the heavy oak door to Izmini's chamber. The exquisite young princess did not acknowledge his greetings, as he bowed low and said in his most charming manner: "Good evening, Princess. I am Prince Philippos from Thessaloniki."

His reward was a cold stare, but this did not disturb Philippos. He found the chest and hid his little sparrow in it. After sitting down, he repeated, "Good evening, chest. Good evening, chest. Good evening, chest."

The chest answered, "Good evening, Master. All this time you have said nothing to me, but instead you've been talking to this stubborn girl."

"Yes, this is so," replied Philippos, "but won't you tell me some little story to amuse me?"

"With pleasure," answered the chest. "Once upon a time there were three brothers. The oldest, a carpenter, found a log and carved the statue of a woman from it. The second brother, a tailor, dressed the statue in beautiful clothes. The third brother, a theology student, prayed to God for a soul for the statue. The statue came to life, and the brothers quarreled about which one should marry the maiden. To whom, Prince, do you think the maiden belongs?"

"To the first brother, the carpenter," answered Philippos. "That is obvious."

"No," said the chest, "she should be married to the tailor."

The princess, who was listening in spite of herself, had grown impatient.

"Oh, this is too much!" she cried out. "The maiden belongs to the man whose prayers gave her a soul, the theology student."

"She speaks! Did you hear that?" gloated Philippos, flinging open the door and running out to the three old hags. But, to his horror, the trio of old women had fallen asleep, and of course they had heard nothing. Philippos returned to the room, found an excuse to remove the sparrow from the chest, and informed Izmini he would return the next night.

The second night, before entering Izmini's chamber, he cautioned the old women to stay awake and listen.

After greeting the princess, Philippos turned to the chest, but saw that Izmini had broken it to pieces. Thinking quickly, he hid the little sparrow under a table. Once again he bowed low to the princess, saying, "Good evening, Princess. I shall talk to the table tonight so you need not say anything."

Turning to the table, he said "good evening" again three times, and when the table answered, Philippos asked for another story.

"Gladly," answered the table. "Once upon a time there was a king who owned a mosquito. The king kept feeding this mosquito until it grew huge. When it died, the king ordered it skinned and its hide hung on a tree in front of the palace. He vowed that any man who could guess what kind of skin it was could have his daughter's hand in marriage. The devil heard of this, and bribed the king's daughter with a golden apple to reveal the secret of the hide. The devil married the princess, taking her to live in a dark cave. The princess was most unhappy there, and she sent a pigeon to her father, begging him to rescue her. When the king learned of his daughter's unhappiness, he called for men to help free the princess. The first man to answer looked like a camel but could run like a hare. The second man was so fast, he could clap the devil in a wine jug before he would know what had happened. The third man could catch a cup of olive oil without spilling a drop, even if it fell from the sky.

"The other two mounted on the camel man, and they rode until they came to the devil's cave. When they reached their destination, the second man put the devil in a wine jug. But the devil broke out, seized the princess, and carried her away in a dark cloud. All three men shot arrows into the air, and one of them hit the devil. The third man caught the princess as she fell from the sky."

"Well," said the table, "to which one of the rescuers does the princess belong?"

"To the man who looked like a camel but ran like a hare," replied the prince.

"No," said the table, "she belongs to the man who put the devil in the jug."

"Oh, you are both wrong," cried out Izmini impatiently. "She belongs to the man who caught her as she fell from the sky."

"Again! She speaks! Did you hear?" shouted Philippos delightedly as he flung open the door. To his consternation the three old crones were again fast asleep outside the door.

Bitterly disappointed, Philippos managed to remove his little sparrow from Izmini's room, vowing to return the next night.

On the third night, Philippos sternly warned the three old women that they would be severely punished if they did not stay

awake this night. They screeched their promises not to fall asleep.

Philippos entered Izmini's room, greeted her kindly, and looked for the table. He found it smashed to pieces. Undaunted, he turned to the chair and hid his little bird under it. To the chair he said three times "good evening" and "Won't you tell me a little story to amuse me?"

"Of course," agreed the chair. "There once were three brothers in love with the same girl. In order to get them to forget her, their father sent each of them to a different land. After three years they returned with precious souvenirs, but still in love with the same young girl. The first brother had found a magic looking glass that reflected all that was happening anywhere in the world. The second brother had found a magic carpet that could fly to the end of the world in two minutes. The third brother had found a magic apple that could bring the dead to life if it were placed under the nose of the corpse.

"A few days after their return, they looked in the magic mirror and saw their beloved dying from a strange illness. They quickly mounted the carpet and flew to her, but, alas, she was dead. The third brother held his magic apple under her nose, and to everyone's amazement she rose again, perfectly well.

"Now, Philippos, to whom does the girl belong?"

"Why to the brother who owned the magic mirror," replied Philippos.

"No! You are wrong!" disputed the chair. "She belongs to the brother who owned the magic carpet."

"You are both wrong," burst out Izmini. "She obviously belongs to the brother who owned the magic apple."

"'Aha!'' shrieked the three old hags, bursting into the room. "Izmini, you have spoken. We shall fetch the king and give him our report."

The grateful king was most happy to give his daughter in marriage to Prince Philippos. As for Izmini, she was no longer silent. Instead, she told everyone how happy she was to be the bride of so clever and handsome a prince.

The good prince gave his little sparrow the choice of remaining with him or taking leave. The sparrow chose freedom, soaring away singing his master's praises.

And so they held a joyous wedding with much feasting and dancing. For the rest of their lives the royal couple lived in love and great happiness.

The Foolish Women

Once upon a time there lived on the island of Cos a man called Basil, whose farm was large and prosperous. One morning, after he left home to tend his olive groves, his wife, Aliki, went to fetch some water from the village well. There she met one of her friends who, noticing Aliki's worried, preoccupied look, asked, "What troubles you so today?"

"Oh," answered Aliki, "it is only that I am so afraid and worried about the safety of my son and my husband."

"But you have no son, and Basil, your good husband, is perfectly safe on the farm," said the puzzled friend.

"Yes, I know that," snapped Aliki. "But what if we did have a son, and what if he and Basil were to have an accident and die?" With this the absurd Aliki burst into tears.

Her friend thought about this for a moment, and soon she, too, began to cry. In a short while the two women were joined by a circle of other village women who were curious to find out what tragedy had occurred. As the silly Aliki sobbingly told her story, the others in turn began to cry. None of the women returned to their homes to finish their chores but sat instead, mourning and weeping over the imaginary deaths. After a while they grew hungry and decided to have a funeral feast. Aliki, supported on either side by sympathetic women, invited them all to her home, where they promptly slaughtered Basil's finest ox.

As the ox crackled invitingly on a spit over the fire, Basil wearily entered his yard. He could hardly believe his eyes when he saw the enormous roasting ox tended by a whole flock of lamenting women.

"Aliki," he demanded, "what is the meaning of all this?"

His wife ran to him with tears streaming down her face as she related the tale of the imaginary accident and deaths.

"These other kind women are preparing the funeral feast for us," reassured Aliki.

Thereupon Basil became so angry he shouted, "I am leaving, and I won't come back until I find in the world two women as silly as you are."

And off he went, too, the very next day to the island of Skyros. There in the market place he noticed a poor woman in

rags, thanking and blessing a richly dressed man.

Basil listened to them as the woman said, "Thank you, kind sir, for offering your help. And I have brought you all my savings, so that no matter how far the journey, you will be able to complete it and return safely with my husband and son."

"My good woman," said the splendidly attired gentleman, "I'm glad you realize the journey to the beyond, to bring back your husband and son, both dead now for five years, will be long and very costly. But I will undertake it for you. As you know, it will be a perilous task, but you must be patient and tell no one about this until my return."

Seizing the woman's money, and with scarcely a glance at her, the man mounted his horse and departed.

"Oh, what a foolish woman," Basil groaned to himself. "She will never see that swindler or her money again!"

But the farmer was not convinced he had seen enough of women's foolishness, so he departed for Pontos. When he arrived there, he walked about until he met a man and his wife, sitting under a tree near a meadow. Basil decided to rest for a while and accepted the man's invitation to join them in a meal of cheese, olives, and wine. Basil noticed, however, that the wife did not eat. Soon the wife strolled away into the meadow, looking about her.

Taking advantage of her absence, the man explained, "My wife refuses to eat her meals with me because I cautioned her about eating too much. But I found the ridiculous woman stuffed herself as soon as I left the house. Today, she has been with me all day, and if she wants to eat, she must eat with me!"

Eventually the wife joined her husband and Basil, and they

sat talking till sundown. By that time the foolish woman was so weak from hunger she could hardly see.

As they walked home, she saw some black beetles crawling along the road and she swooped some up, saying, "Oh, my little olives, you had no feet, yet you grew feet to come to meet me, so that I might crunch you."

Her husband stopped her from eating the beetles, and when at last they reached their cottage, they sat down and had their evening meal together. The wife promised her husband she would never again be guilty of such absurdities.

Basil departed, laughing at the lesson the man had taught his foolish wife.

"Well," he mused, "perhaps I have seen enough of foolish women to know there are others like Aliki. I will return to Cos."

When Basil reached home, Aliki vowed there would be no more nonsense. The next day Basil bought some meat and gave it to Aliki to cook for their dinner. When he returned later in the evening, he found no dinner, but Aliki assured him he would be surprised to see what she had taught their best sheep.

Aliki sat down at the table and commanded, "Sheep, did you hear Basil? Cook the meat!"

The sheep, of course, paid no attention, grazing patiently instead on some straw.

Aliki began to berate the sheep, and even gave it a few slaps.

Basil interrupted her tirade, saying, "Well, enough of your scolding the sheep. Leave it to me. I will punish it."

Throwing the sheep on Aliki's back, Basil took up a heavy stick and began striking so that he missed the sheep but rained blows on Aliki's back.

All the time he was beating Aliki, Basil kept saying, "You bad sheep, why didn't you obey my wife and do her work instead of just grazing like any ordinary sheep?"

After Aliki had gotten many a blow, she begged Basil to stop, promising she would change.

"Never again," she gasped, "will I be guilty of any more foolishness, and I will do all the cooking and not leave anything to the sheep."

From then on Aliki kept her word, and for the rest of their lives they lived in love and happiness.

The Thief in
the King's Treasury

Once, long ago, on the island of Cyprus, there lived a robber who had grown rich and prosperous. Since he had no heir, he decided to ask his poor brother if he might adopt one of his three sons. The father of the three lads was delighted with this proposal, and one fine morning he sent his three boys to their uncle's home.

Now the uncle intended that the youth he chose to be his heir would also be of help as his partner. Therefore he was determined to test the cunning and resourcefulness of each of his nephews. To do this, he hung a twig with a ring of cake on it from a rafter high in the ceiling of a chamber in his house. There seemed to be no way to reach the morsel of cake, and indeed it would require a very shrewd lad to bring it down.

"My dear nephew," said the uncle to the oldest, "I will leave you in this chamber for the night. By tomorrow morning I shall expect you to have eaten that delicious cake for your breakfast."

The next morning the robber found his nephew sitting on the floor gazing up at the undisturbed cake. The uncle sent this boy home to his father, while later that evening he instructed the second nephew to eat the cake for his breakfast. But in the morning, the second youth was worn out from his unsuccessful efforts, and he, too, was sent back home.

Third and youngest of the nephews was a lad called Georgi, as ingenious and clever as he was kind. As soon as his uncle left him, he set about trying to bring the cake down. When morning came, his astonished uncle found him munching the last crumbs of the cake.

"Well done, my boy!" cried the uncle. "You shall most certainly be my heir and my partner, too. But how did you manage to bring the cake down?"

Flashing a triumphant grin, Georgi explained, "In your kitchen, uncle, I found a large sponge which I steeped in water. I kept throwing the wet sponge against the cake. As it became wetter it also softened; finally it crumbled and fell down. So you see, it really was simple."

With delighted laughter, the uncle clapped his nephew on the back, saying, "Come, my boy, let us seek a fortune. Perhaps we will find something worthy of our efforts."

Before responding, Georgi thought for a moment of the wealthy king of Cyprus and the taxes he collected from his subjects. This king managed to exact so much from the people that most were left bereft of everything except the barest necessities.

"If only I could manage to get some of the gold back into the hands of the poor people in our village," mused Georgi.

Then he said aloud, "Uncle, let us not be bothered with trifles. Instead, tonight let us go and rob the king's treasury."

"The king's treasury!" shrieked the uncle, jumping up from his chair. "How in the world do you propose we do that?"

"Just provide me with a sack, some rope, and a hook, then you shall see," replied Georgi.

Later that night a calm Georgi, followed by his curious uncle, silently glided along the marble walls of the king's treasure house. While his uncle stared in fascination, Georgi attached the hook to the rope, threw the hooked end so that it stuck securely to the edge of the roof, and nimbly climbed up the rope to the treasury roof. Leaning over, he helped his uncle who, with much huffing and puffing, did the same.

After some searching, Georgi pried a loose flagstone from the roof, leaving a hole large enough for him to enter the storeroom. He lowered himself by means of his rope, taking a sack with him. When he had filled the sack with gold, his uncle pulled it up. Then in a twinkling Georgi hauled himself up, replaced the flagstone, and hurried himself and his uncle home.

For three straight nights the two continued to enter the treasury, carrying away enough gold to all but empty the king's storeroom. While his uncle insisted on keeping his share, Georgi

refused to keep any of the gold. Rather, he secretly distributed the money to families in the village who needed it desperately.

On the fourth day, the king, needing gold, visited his treasury. When he saw the nearly empty room his rage was boundless. He stamped his feet, tore his hair, and howled loud and long for the guards. Together they searched everyone in the palace, but there was not a trace of the money or the thief.

After much scurrying and worrying, the king and his prime minister decided to set a trap. They filled the treasury with more gold, making sure all the people in the palace and in the village knew about it. This time, however, the guards covered the floor with sticky pitch so that anyone stepping there would be held fast.

Georgi and his uncle, hearing of the refilled treasury, decided to visit the roof later that night. As Georgi was about to descend into the storeroom, he smelled the pitch and refused to go down.

"Bah!" said his uncle, whose greed had overcome his caution. "You are imagining things. Let me go."

As soon as he touched the floor, the unlucky man was stuck fast. Horrified, Georgi lowered the rope to him and tried to pull him free, but in vain. The guards, hearing the uncle thrashing around, flung open the doors.

"Run, Georgi, run," pleaded his uncle, as the guards threw down wooden planks to reach him and capture their quarry.

Fleeing from the treasury house, Georgi barely escaped, arriving home to break the unhappy news to his aunt. They both wept bitterly, knowing the king would order the robber's death. Indeed, hardly had dawn broken when the news reached them of the uncle's execution. At the palace, however, there was only unconfined joy as the monarch rushed about giving orders for a great feast to celebrate the demise of the thief.

But while the king and his court were feasting, Georgi decided it was time to distribute more of the king's gold to a very poor family beset with illness and grief. And so once again, late in the night, he raided the treasury, managing to slip away with a bag of gold. The next morning the guards inspected the storeroom and reported the theft to the astonished king.

Again there was much agitation and cogitation, resulting in a royal proclamation. The square in front of the market, decreed the king, was to be covered with gold coins. Anyone trying to steal the coins would be judged the thief and punished for the crime of robbing the treasury.

"What a wonderful chance to get more gold," thought Georgi when he heard this, "and in daylight, too!"

He went home, fetched what he needed, and assured his aunt he would soon have more gold coins to help at least one other needy family. As he approached the square, he smeared the soles of his shoes with fish glue. Then he walked back and forth on the gold coins in full view of the fiercest palace guards. After such a walk he removed the coins from his soles in a place where no one could see him. Then he went back for more.

Later that night, the captain of the guards brought all the coins to the king and his prime minister for counting. When they finished, the king turned purple with rage.

"More than two dozen coins are missing!" he screamed, gnashing his teeth. "You and all your men will be fined triple the amount stolen, for allowing the thief to escape from under your noses!"

63

Once more the frantic sovereign pondered his problem. He finally devised what he considered a foolproof scheme for capturing this thief. He ordered a camel to be loaded with jewels, silks, and ivory. The captain and several of his guards were commanded to lead the camel into the market place. The thief, thought the king, would not be able to resist stealing such a prize.

"Now, mind you," exhorted the king, "keep your wits about you, for the thief is bound to try to capture this treasure. This time if he escapes, you will be fearfully punished."

As the guards led the camel on the road toward the market place, they passed Georgi's house. The young thief's eyes gleamed as he speculated on how he would capture this bounty.

Whistling merrily to himself, he changed into a wine vendor's clothes, hoisted a barrel of wine on his shoulder, and ran into the street crying, "Wine for sale, one half *drachma* for a cup! Who will buy my wine?"

Finding the wine so cheap, the thirsty guards eagerly bought many cups—becoming so tipsy they forgot all about the camel. Georgi's aunt merely had to open the gate and the camel meandered inside her yard. Meanwhile, the guards had become so drunk they lay down in the street and fell asleep.

While they peacefully snored on, Georgi and his aunt unloaded the camel, hid its precious cargo, killed the beast, then melted down its fat. They had been able to fill two huge jars with camel grease when the guards awoke from their slumber. They returned, shamefaced and quaking, to the king. Of course he ordered them all into prison.

"We'll soon get to the bottom of this," the prime minister

assured the enraged king. "To hide the camel in a small cottage, the culprits have probably killed the beast and melted it down, intending to make good use of its fat. But I have a plan by which we may soon discover who has committed this outrage. We'll send an old woman from house to house to beg for a crockful of camel's grease to use as medicine. Wherever she finds it, you may be sure we'll find the thief!"

An old, trusted servant was dispatched on this errand. When she came to Georgi's house, his aunt gave her a crockful of grease. In order not to forget the house, she dipped her hand in the grease and marked the door with it as she left.

Soon after, Georgi came home and noticed the camel's grease on the door.

"Ah, my aunt, in giving away the camel's grease, you have given us away," he sighed. "But wait, I have an idea that may save us. Give me some of that grease. I'll be back as soon as I have visited the other doors of our village."

The old woman, meanwhile, hurried back to the palace, triumphantly reporting what she had done. The gratified king and all his court hurried out to confront the thief. But to their dismay and disgust, they saw all the doors marked with camel's grease, making it impossible to find the culprit's house.

"He won't get by me this next time," swore the furious king.

Then the sovereign issued another proclamation. He promised the thief gifts for his cleverness if he would present himself in the main square on Saturday noon.

"Aha," thought Georgi, "well, I can certainly use more gifts. There are many more poor villagers that need my help. I shall most certainly be there."

Before joining all the excited, chattering people in the crowded square, Georgi took the precaution of dressing himself in the same uniform as that of the soldiers who were on guard outside the square.

When he was in the midst of the townfolk, Georgi cried out, "Here I am, here is the thief!"

The king shouted in return, "Arrest that man!"

Georgi joined the soldiers charging into the crowd, also shouting, "Arrest him! Arrest him!"

He darted in and out among the bewildered soldiers shouting orders and causing them to chase one another. After thoroughly confusing them, he ran off, laughing so hard that all the buttons on his uniform popped off.

The next morning the people were greeted by still another decree from their humiliated, exasperated ruler. If the thief would confess his crimes to the king's daughter, promised the monarch, he could have the princess for his wife and become heir to the throne.

Georgi was overjoyed to hear of this, and he decided to visit the princess. He took care, however, to take along a carved wooden hand covered with a glove, just in case of an unforeseen emergency. He made his way that night in darkness to the palace window where he could dimly see the waiting princess. He had just begun to relate his exploits to her when she interrupted him, and begged leave to hold so famous a hand as his while he continued. Georgi gladly obliged, but as soon as the princess took his hand she began screaming for help. The king, prime minister, and all the soldiers came running, brandishing their scimitars. But, alas, all that the princess seized was the wooden hand covered with Georgi's glove, and an old one at that.

"Well," sighed the king, "this thief is too clever, even for a king. This time I shall truly reward him and I shall keep my promise."

So that all would know that this time he really intended to give his daughter's hand in marriage as well as make the thief his heir, the king solemnly vowed in church before the priest that he would keep his word.

Messengers went out to every corner of the island asking the thief to claim his reward. Now at last Georgi presented himself at the palace, where he was warmly welcomed.

Then the king ordered a feast whose like had never before been seen. People from all the villages and towns were invited, and they ate, drank, and were merry. Georgi and the princess were wed, and they lived happily for many years. When the king died, Georgi ruled the land so wisely and well that it became a realm of peace and high contentment for many years.

Truth or Lies

To approach Crete for the first time is to be filled with delight, for the island shines like a precious stone in the deep blue sea. Its rocky hills, green forests, and snug pastures are bathed in the clear golden sunshine that adds luster to its many beauties. This shimmering, peaceful scene gave no hint, however, of the fearful adventure that would befall two strong lads from the tiny island of Karpathos, and settle for them for all time which is the stronger—the truth or a lie.

These stalwart boys left their homes to seek their fortunes in

Crete, where they had heard there was money to be earned. As they prepared to board a *caique* for the journey, their mothers gave them advice, each according to her own beliefs.

"Dimitri, my son," cautioned Maria, mother of the first boy, "never sit idle. Work for any wage offered, even if it is only one *drachma*."

Katina, the second boy's mother, had another type of warning. "Nicholas," she said, "do not work for less than twenty *drachmas* a week. You'll have plenty of offers. Accept only the best."

And so they approached Crete for the first time. Once they reached their destination, Dimitri found many jobs—mending fishermen's nets, tending olive groves, hewing timber in the forests, and herding sheep in the pastures. He labored at everything and earned good wages for his cheerfulness and willingness.

Nicholas, alas, did not fare so well. Many of his would-be employers laughed at his demand for twenty *drachmas*. He often had to search long and hard before he could find the work he liked. And often the wages were much less than what he had expected.

A year passed, and Dimitri longed to visit his home. He thought happily of the six hundred *drachmas* he had earned, and how surprised his mother would be at this present. Sitting contentedly on the docks, he waited for the *caique* to carry him to his island home of Karpathos.

Not so content, though, was Nicholas, who would have to stay behind. He had not been able to earn enough to feed himself properly, much less to bring home money to his family.

With bitter envy, he looked at his happy friend. Deep in his heart he felt he was much more able than Dimitri. And so he devised a clever scheme to trick his companion into giving him his money.

"Dimitri, you are the wiser one," he said. "Therefore, tell me which is the stronger, lying or telling the truth?"

"Telling the truth," firmly answered Dimitri.

"I say lying!" came back Nicholas.

The two boys argued heatedly, as Nicholas had planned.

Finally he said, "Well, since you are so sure of yourself, let us make a bet. We will ask three people their opinions. If they agree with me, you must give me your six hundred *drachmas*."

Dimitri was so sure truth was the stronger that he agreed to this. The boys did not have long to wait before settling the argument. Three travelers disembarked from one of the boats and approached them.

The first man was an old priest. His long white beard reached over his black gown. His face was lined and gnarled from care and old age. On his white head perched a high stovepipe hat. He carried a staff to help him walk.

"Good Father, can you settle a question for us?" asked Nicholas. "Which is the stronger, truth or lies?"

The old priest thought for a long time before replying. Then he shook his head and said sadly, "I have seen much of this world. Alas, my son, unfortunately lying is the stronger."

Nicholas then turned to the second man, a Royal Palace guardsman, making his way from Athens. He wore his white pleated skirt, the *fustanella*, and his tasseled cap. His fierce black mustache twitched up and down as Nicholas repeated to him the important question.

"Humph! You silly boy!" barked the retired guard, "Why, lying is the stronger in this world." Then he stomped away, deep in his own thoughts.

Finally Nicholas turned to the third traveler. He was a young sheep herder, coming from a distant market place. From the sour look on his face the boys could guess how his trading had gone.

When he heard Nicholas' question he answered with a sneer, "Why, lying is the stronger, of course!"

Without a word, Nicholas turned to Dimitri and held out his hand. Dimitri sadly gave him the money for which he had worked so hard.

Now it was Nicholas' turn to grin happily. As he jumped aboard the *caique*, he gaily waved good-by to Dimitri. Nicholas was overjoyed at the thought of all the tales he would tell of grateful employers who had paid him for jobs he had carefully chosen to do.

Dimitri watched the *caique* sail for home. Then he wandered unhappily and aimlessly along the beach. When night came and the full moon rose, he found himself on a lonely stretch of beach with no houses in sight. The only shelter he could find was an old, rotted boat turned upside down. Feeling miserable and forlorn, he crawled under it and went to sleep.

Awakened by voices a few hours later, Dimitri peered up through the cracked ribs of the boat. He saw three demons sitting on the keel of the boat. The ugly creatures were cackling over their plans. One demon told how, during the next day, he would set two brothers to quarreling. As a result the brothers would be so busy they would be sure to miss church.

The second demon shrilled with joy as he described his plan to plague men. He would stir up a violent storm three nights hence. The storm would be so sudden that fishermen would not have time to save their little boats from total destruction.

The third demon shrieked with glee as he described the spell he had already cast over a princess who lived in a nearby village. She would not be able to move for the next seven years unless someone found a magic olive branch in the chest in her room. If the branch were waved over her three times, the princess would be cured.

The demons cackled happily over their plans. As dawn came they scampered away and disappeared. Dimitri then crawled out from under the boat and hurried to the house of the quarreling brothers. He reconciled them and sent them off to church. Next he went to the wharves, where he found the fishermen. While they listened, Dimitri warned them of the coming storm. They believed the earnest boy and assured him they would take proper care of their boats in time.

Lastly, Dimitri went to the king's window and cried out, "I am a doctor, who can use my services?"

The desperate king heard him and had his servants bring Dimitri before him. The lad assured the king he was a doctor and could cure the princess. As soon as he was shown into her room he ordered everyone out. Then he quickly found the olive branch in the large oak chest. Three times he waved the branch over the princess, and just as the demon predicted, she awoke and jumped up from her bewitched sleep.

The king and all his court wept with joy when they saw the lovely princess restored to health. As a reward the grateful king

gave Dimitri two horses, their saddlebags laden with gold.

Thus the lad was able to return to his mother with a fortune. They paid all their debts, and Dimitri's little sisters were assured of large dowries. There was even plenty of money left for a fine new house.

The news of all this prosperity quickly spread throughout the village. When Nicholas heard the stories, he was once again deeply envious of his friend. He felt he had been cheated of some good fortune that had come to the less clever Dimitri. Nicholas promptly visited Dimitri and begged him to tell his secret.

After hesitating awhile, Dimitri decided to tell the truth. He explained how he had overheard the demons and upset their evil plans.

"If I should go there and hide underneath the boat, might I not also gain something?" asked Nicholas.

"In truth, I do not know," answered Dimitri.

Nicholas decided to return to Crete to try his luck with the demons. It was once again the time of the full moon. On the deserted beach he found the overturned boat and, when night came, he crept under it. A short time later the three demons scrambled up the side of the boat and settled themselves on the upturned keel. Their voices were full of complaint.

"Last month I set two brothers quarreling so they would not go to church. But a young lad helped them to make up their argument and sent them off to worship," wailed the first demon.

The second demon moaned, "The storm I sent last month did no damage to the fishermen's boats. Someone had forewarned them, and their boats were safely moored."

The third demon groaned, "I cast a spell on the king's daughter for the next seven years, but last month someone found the magic olive branch and cured her with it. Who can possibly know our secrets?"

Just then Nicholas sneezed. The demons shrieked. "There is someone underneath this boat listening to us!"

They jumped up and lifted the boat. There on the sand they saw Nicholas all curled up and staring at them.

"Are you the clever one," they howled, "who spoiled all our plans?"

Now Nicholas was a lad who could not resist lying, particularly about things he had not done, and especially about things to show off his cleverness. So he stood up brazenly and said, "Yes, it was I who tricked you—three times."

Before Nicholas could say another word, the horrible demons picked him up and tossed him into the deep sea, from which he never returned. Thus it came about that Nicholas proved it was truth and not lies that indeed was the stronger.

Sources of Folk Tales from the Greek World

The Cyclades / islands of the Central Aegean. The inner ring of this archipelago circles the holy island of Delos like a chaplet, hence the name "Cyclades." The most important island in antiquity, Delos was the birthplace of the god Apollo. In modern Greek the island group is called Kikládes.

Cyprus / an island at the eastern end of the Mediterranean Sea, off the coast of Syria. Once a British colony, Cyprus has been independent since 1960.

Epirus / a country of ancient Greece, bordering on the Ionian Sea. It is known as Ipiros in modern Greek, and now the area includes part of northwestern Greece and southern Albania.

Karpathos / a Greek island, one of the Dodecanese, which is located between Rhodes and the eastern end of Crete. Its ancient name was Carpathus.

Kos / also called Cos, this is the largest of the Dodecanese Islands, belonging to Greece and located in the southeastern Aegean Sea. Rhodes is the administrative center of the island group. Kos is the birthplace of Hippocrates.

Lemnos / a Greek island in the Aegean Sea, off the western coast of Turkey. It is well known in mythology as the volcanic island where *Haphaestus*, the god of fire and forges, married Aphrodite. Its modern Greek name is Límnos.

Macedonia / a region in southern Europe in the Balkan Peninsula, covering parts of Greece, Yugoslavia, and Bulgaria. Salonika is the chief city in the Greek section today. The ancient kingdom of Macedon reached its height under Alexander the Great in the fourth century B.C.

Náxos / the largest of the Cyclades Islands in the southern Aegean Sea, Náxos belongs to Greece. In antiquity it was famous for wines and fertility, and according to legend Theseus, after slaying the Minotaur, abandoned the sleeping Ariadne on Naxos. She was soon consoled by Dionysus. The story of *Ariadne in Naxos* is the subject of a famous opera by Richard Strauss.

Thrace / a region in the Balkan Peninsula north of the Aegean Sea. As an ancient country, it extended to the Danube, but now Thrace is a small area divided by Greece (Western Thrace) and Turkey (Eastern Thrace).

About the Author

Rose Neufeld was educated at Hunter College and New York University and now teaches in the New York City school system. She enjoys traveling and when she returns likes to prepare exotic dishes from the countries she has visited. It was while she and her husband, a photojournalist and documentary film maker, were in Greece that Mrs. Neufeld collected the folk tales for this book.

About the Artist

Marjorie Auerbach studied graphic art and painting at the University of Wisconsin and Cooper Union before turning to free-lance illustration. She and her husband, an art director, have traveled in Mexico and Europe and now live in New York City with Andrea, their small daughter. This is the fifth book which Mrs. Auerbach has illustrated for Knopf. She is also the author of two Knopf juveniles: *Seven Uncles Came to Dinner* and *King Lavra and the Barber*.

The text of this book was set in Linotype Palatino, a contemporary type designed in Germany in 1950 by Hermann Zapf. Modern type design occasionally reverts to the ancient Venetian masters for inspiration, and although this face bears the name of a famous penman of the sixteenth century, its design ranks it among Venetian romans, as is indicated by the broad design of the capitals and some of the lower case. Palatino is, nevertheless, an up-to-date, original type, not a mechanical copy of an historical type. Its elegance, weight, and letter forms make it particularly suitable for use with woodcuts.

Composed by Brown Bros. Linotypers, New York City
Printed by Jenkins—Universal Corp., Timonium, Maryland
Bound by Jenkins—Universal Corp., Richmond, Virginia
Typography by Atha Tehon